Backyard
Breakfast

To my favorite little boys—
John, Franklin, and Samuel

Written by **BETSY HIBBETT**
Illustrated by **ELENA VOROBEVA**

Published by Argyle Fox Publishing | argylefoxpublishing.com
ISBN 978-1-953259-21-9 (Paperback)
ISBN 978-1-953259-22-6 (Hardcover)

My little one is up, ready to play,
Hoping to find a fun start to the day.

I know—let's make breakfast the backyard way!

The chickens are up and squawking away.
We scatter the feed and change out their hay.

Then check in their coop.
What did they lay?

Look! There are eggs—

brown,

white,

green,

and speckled.

Place them in the basket, beside the freckled.

Our dog is up and ready to play.

Throw him a ball,
watch him run away.

Running, running back. Hooray!

Let's check the garden to see what is new.

Tomatoes,

peppers,

and strawberries, too!

Have a small taste but don't eat it all yet.
Put it in your basket before you forget!

We dig up the weeds to help our plants grow,
Make room for next season's seeds that we'll sow:

Lettuce, broccoli, and white cauliflower.
Turn on the hose and give them a shower.

Honeybees are up and flying around.
If quiet, we may hear their buzzing sound.

Bees on that flower, they're out of their hive,
Searching for pollen they need to survive.

We put on our bee suits to see what we've got.
Don't want to get stung, 'cause that hurts a lot!

Look! So much honey—yellow and delicious.
All of this food is so good and nutritious.

Zinnias for the table—pink, orange, and red.
Aren't you so glad we got out of our beds?

Pick up your basket and bring it inside.
Time for a feast that our backyard supplied.

Yes, it takes work. Yes, it takes time.
But I promise this meal will be simply sublime.

Eggs to scramble and drizzle with honey,
Veggies to cook and go in your tummy,

Lots of fresh fruit—all so very yummy!

Our morning's work feels a lot like play
When we do breakfast the backyard way!

CPSIA information can be obtained
at www.ICGtesting.com
Printed in the USA
BVHW021910200422
634698BV00030B/797